Read, Search & Find®

Under the Sea

Kidsbooks®

Illustrations Copyright © 2012, Orpheus Books Ltd
2 Church Green Witney, Oxon OX28 4AW

Illustrated by Peter Dennis (Linda Rogers Associates)
Written by Tracy N. Rogers, MS, Marine Science Educator

Text and Design Copyright © 2012, 2014, 2015 Kidsbooks, LLC.
Read, Search & Find is a registered trademark of Kidsbooks, LLC.
3535 West Peterson Avenue
Chicago, IL 60659

Printed in China
011503026JS

Visit us at www.kidsbooks.com

Contents

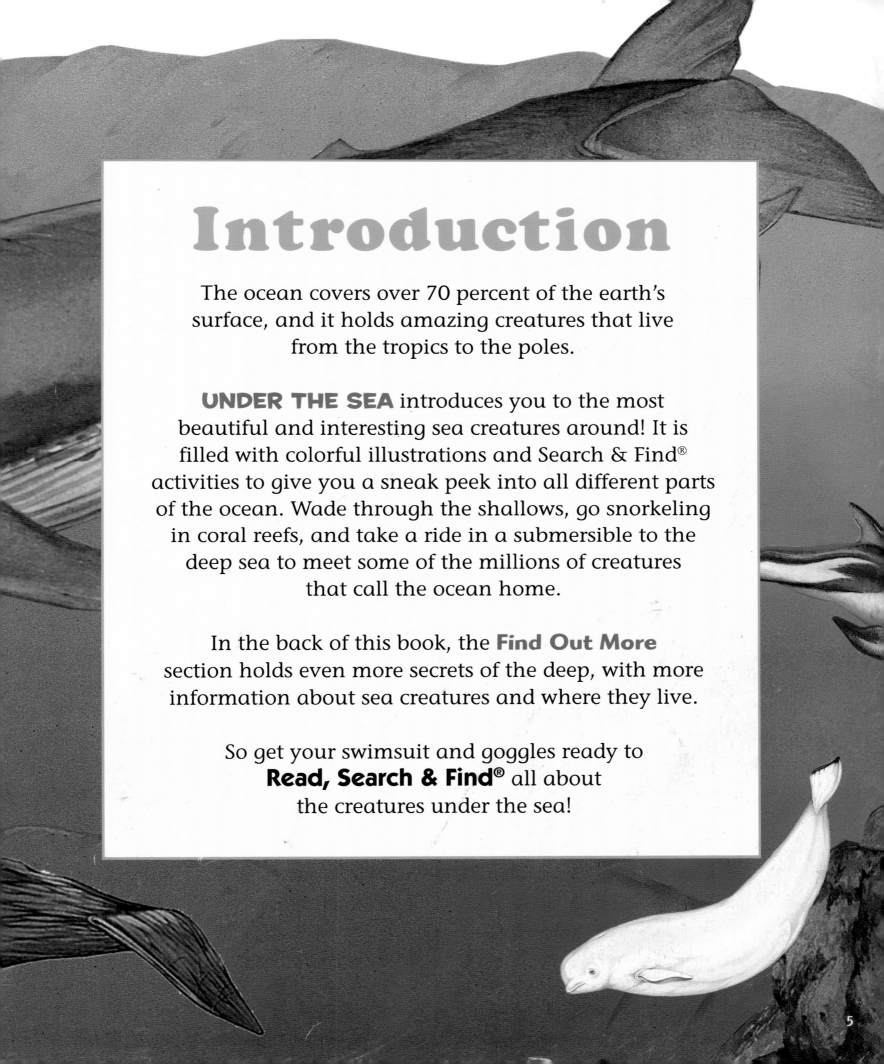

Introduction

The ocean covers over 70 percent of the earth's surface, and it holds amazing creatures that live from the tropics to the poles.

UNDER THE SEA introduces you to the most beautiful and interesting sea creatures around! It is filled with colorful illustrations and Search & Find® activities to give you a sneak peek into all different parts of the ocean. Wade through the shallows, go snorkeling in coral reefs, and take a ride in a submersible to the deep sea to meet some of the millions of creatures that call the ocean home.

In the back of this book, the **Find Out More** section holds even more secrets of the deep, with more information about sea creatures and where they live.

So get your swimsuit and goggles ready to **Read, Search & Find®** all about the creatures under the sea!

Open-Ocean Creatures

Animals that live in the open waters of the ocean are able to travel great distances. These animals migrate to find food or other animals of their own species. Since there is no shelter in the open ocean, the animals have special adaptations that allow them to survive. Many of the animals have torpedo-shaped bodies that allow them to travel swiftly through the water. Some can even leap out of the water, like the flying fish and the blue marlin.

Search & find the animals below.

Manta Ray

The manta ray is the largest ray in the world. It averages over 20 feet wide and can weigh up to 3,000 pounds.

Squid

The squid is related to the octopus and has eight arms. It can also change color to appear invisible to its predators!

Flying Fish

This fish has large fins that help it glide over the water for up to 100 feet. It can also leap out of the water to escape predators!

Hawksbill Sea Turtle

This critically endangered sea turtle has a sharp beak that allows it to eat hard sea sponges found on coral reefs.

Blue Marlin

This large fish (can weigh up to 2,000 pounds!) dashes through schools of smaller fish and wounds them with its spear, making them easier to catch.

Tuna

This yellowfin tuna is one of many types of tuna. It can travel very fast for long distances, and prefers to live in warm waters.

Mahi-mahi

Mahi-mahi is Hawaiian for *strong-strong*. This beautifully colored fish can swim over 50 miles per hour!

Find Out More on page 26

Coral Reef

Coral reefs exist in warm, tropical waters all over the world. Tiny animals called corals slowly build the reefs with their bodies. When the reef becomes large enough, other organisms move in and make themselves at home. This can take hundreds of years. This reef is an example of a healthy reef, because it has living coral, lots of fish, and even sharks. Coral reefs are like underwater cities: There are many colors, many jobs to do, and never a dull moment!

Search & find the following animals.

Lionfish

When the lionfish wants to scare other animals, it makes itself look bigger by stretching out its fins, which resemble a lion's mane.

Puffer Fish

This fish has spines in its skin that it can push out to protect itself.

Parrot Fish

The parrot fish has hard, white teeth that look like a beak. They allow the fish to eat the part of the reef that is hard as bone.

Sea Horse

This fish uses its long tail to wrap around coral and plants so it will not get swept away in the current.

Moray Eel

This eel has a second set of jaws in its throat that it can thrust forward into its mouth when it's time to eat!

Cowfish

The cowfish is also known as a boxfish. Can you tell why?

Find Out More
on page 27

Deep-Sea Life

Not much is known about the depths of the ocean. We do know that it's very dark and that there are very peculiar animals living in this sunless sea. You may notice that many of the animals have built-in "lightbulbs" in their fins. These are special organs that glow. Scientists think they use this light to attract other animals closer so they can eat them. If you've ever seen an insect fly toward a light outside, you can imagine how small fish could be attracted to the light on these animals' bodies.

Search & find the following creatures.

Dumbo Octopus
This octopus gets its name from the two fins on its head, which flop like an elephant's ears.

Viperfish
This fish is said to have a bottomless stomach. Since food is scarce in the deep sea, it eats all it can when it does find food.

Gulper Eel
This eel swims into groups of small shrimp and opens its mouth, which acts like a huge net that captures many shrimp in one gulp.

10

Sixgill Shark

This shark gets its name from the number of gill slits on the side of its body. Most sharks have only five slits.

Jelly

What most people call a *jellyfish* scientists call a *jelly*, since it's not a true fish. The jelly has been around since before the dinosaurs!

Anglerfish

The anglerfish has a unique way of attracting fish to its mouth for an easy meal. Can you find it?

Hatchetfish

This fish resembles a hatchet (a type of ax). Most hatchetfish are only between 1 and 6 inches long.

Find Out More
on page 27

11

Life on the Ocean Bed

Animals that live on the ocean floor have special adaptations that allow them to walk along the seabed and hold on to the rocks and sand. Many of the animals that live on the ocean bed are the ocean's recyclers: they are able to eat and use particles that fall through the water that would otherwise go to waste.

Search & find the following creatures.

Venus Flower Basket

This sponge lives deep in the ocean and creates a skeleton out of sand that is as strong as glass.

Tripod Fish

This fish uses its special fins to walk along the ocean floor, and maybe to feel vibrations of other fish, either to eat or to escape from them.

Brittle Star

This animal has five arms coming out of a central disk. If a brittle star loses an arm, it can grow it back.

Find Out More on page 28

Sea Cucumber

If this squishy animal gets scared, it can eject its slimy stomach to distract its predator. It can also grow back an injured stomach or arms!

Sea Anemone

This animal has no bones and is related to the jelly. It has the same kind of stinging cells on the top of its body as jellies do on their tentacles.

Sea Pen

The sea pen resembles an old-fashioned feather pen that was dipped in ink in order to write. It is related to coral.

Goosefish

The goosefish, also called a monkfish, has a very large mouth that allows it to swallow prey as big as itself.

Spotted Ratfish

The ratfish is more closely related to sharks than to other bony fish. It can be found from the surface all the way down to 3,000 feet!

Urchin

This spiny animal has specialized tube feet that allow it to walk along the surface and stick to rocks.

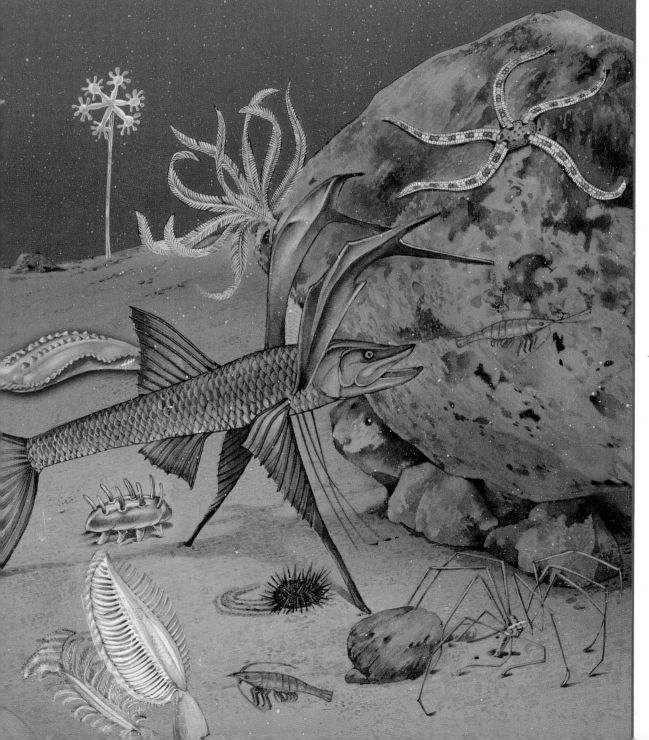

Sharks and More

Sharks and rays are types of fish that do not have bones. Their bodies are made of cartilage, the same type of material that makes up your nose and ears. These animals are cold-blooded, which means their bodies take on the temperature of their surroundings. Humans and other mammals are warm-blooded; we can stay warmer than the air around us. Scientists have discovered hundreds of types of sharks and rays.

Search & find the animals below.

Great White
These famous predators of the sea have very strong jaws and eat large fish, other sharks, and even whales.

Hammerhead
This shark's big head is equipped with special sensors to find its favorite prey, stingrays. It can find them hiding under the sand and then hold them down with its head while it eats!

Nurse Shark
A nurse shark spends most of its days hiding in underwater caves, resting, and then hunts and eats at night.

Goblin Shark
This strange-looking shark uses its long snout like a big antenna to detect its prey moving in the water.

Sawfish
This ray uses its long nose to dig in the soil to find and eat small animals.

Whale Shark
This is the largest species of shark in the world, around 40 feet long and weighing about 10,000 pounds!

Find Out More on page 28

Whales

There are two types of whales: baleen whales and toothed whales. Baleen whales' mouths don't have teeth, but instead have baleen, a hairlike strainer that is used to capture the small microscopic animals and plants they eat, called plankton. Toothed whales have teeth and eat larger animals, like fish and other mammals. Dolphins are a type of toothed whale.

Search & find the whales below.

Blue Whale

This baleen whale averages around 70 to 90 feet long and can weigh 200,000 to 300,000 pounds!

Humpback Whale

This baleen whale blows a ring of bubbles called a bubble net to capture plankton and make it easier for the whale to eat them in one gulp.

White-sided Dolphin

This dolphin lives in groups of up to 500 individuals that travel and hunt together.

Common Dolphin

It's easy to spot the common dolphin in the sea. It has a beautiful yellow patch on the side of its body.

Narwhal

This toothed whale may have been mistaken for a unicorn. It has a 9-foot-long tooth that comes right out of its head.

Beaked Whale

The beaked whale has a long mouth that resembles a bird beak, and its teeth remain hidden under its gums.

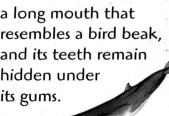

Find Out More on page 29

Seashore

At the seashore, the tide comes in and out twice a day in most parts of the world. At low tide, tide pools are left behind as the ocean moves away from the sandy shore or rocky coast. Some animals, like fish, are trapped in the pools as the tide moves out and stay there until it moves back in to give them a chance to swim back to sea. Other animals, like snails, limpets, mussels, and sea stars, may spend their whole lives in a tide pool.

Search & find the following creatures.

Blenny

A male blenny makes a circular nest in the sand. If a female blenny likes it, she will lay her eggs in it.

Oystercatcher

The oystercatcher has a special beak that allows it to pry open the shells of clams, mussels, and—you guessed it—oysters.

Find Out More
on page 29

18

Bladder Wrack

This type of algae, or seaweed, has little air pockets that help it float when it's submerged in water.

Limpet

This type of snail has a domed shell and lives on rocks. Although they move around during the day looking for food, they always return to the same spot each night.

Crab

All types of crabs live in tide pools. They can crawl under rocks, dart into holes, and walk all over the tide pool by moving sideways.

Hermit Crab

This crab moves from small shells to larger shells as it grows. It usually lives inside empty snail shells.

Sea Lettuce

This seaweed resembles lettuce growing in a garden. It needs sunlight to grow and is usually found in shallow water.

Blue Mussels

Blue mussels grow in clusters. They eat by filtering water through their shells and eating the tiny organisms it holds.

Kelp Forest

These underwater forests are named for giant kelp, a kind of seaweed, that grows in large numbers. Most kelp forests occur close to the shore on the west coast of North and South America. There are a few in northeastern North America as well as in the Southern Ocean. They are teeming with life, from the boneless sea urchin to marine mammals like the sea otter and seal.

Search & find the animals below.

Sheepshead

This fish protects kelp forests by eating urchins, which eat kelp.

Cabezon
This sculpin fish lays eggs that are poisonous to humans and many other animals.

Kelp Wrasse

The kelp wrasse can stretch out its lips and take in large prey that other fish its size cannot.

Sea Otter
This mammal eats urchins. The otter will place a rock or a shell on its chest and bang the urchin against it until it cracks open.

Garibaldi
This looks like a large goldfish but is territorial and aggressive.

Spiny Lobster

This lobster flips its large back tail to swim backward away from predators.

California Sea Lion
This animal hides from predators and rests in these underwater forests.

Find Out More
on page 30

Antarctic Waters

The cold waters of the South Pole host a variety of creatures that have adapted to live in such extreme temperatures. The whales, seals, and penguins have blubber, a layer of fat that acts as insulation against the cold. Penguins also have a way of waterproofing their feathers, which keeps them from getting too cold.

Search & find the animals below.

Emperor Penguin

This adult penguin is 3½ feet tall and weighs over 60 pounds.

Great Albatross

The great albatross is the largest flying bird, with a wingspan over 10 feet wide. They can fly great distances without touching the ground.

Petrel

This bird spends most of its life at sea, only returning to land to nest.

Weddell Seal

This seal has dark fur on the top of its body and is spotted on its sides and belly.

Adelie Penguin

This penguin lives on the outer edge of the ice since they prefer to build their nests in a warmer area.

Chinstrap Penguin

This penguin looks like it's wearing a hat with a strap that goes under its head.

Find Out More on page 30

Hydrothermal Vents

Deep on the ocean floor are places where the ocean water boils. There are cracks in Earth's crust where magma from the core turns the otherwise frigid water into a hot tub—water near the vents can be over 700°F! Creatures that live around hydrothermal vents can be very strange, and scientists can only see them from the safety of a submarine. They collect samples to take back to the surface to study, but the creatures are used to deep, dark, chemical-filled water, which makes it hard to study how they live and act in a lab.

Search & find the following creatures.

Deep-sea Octopus
Although it appears white in this picture, in real life this octopus is most likely completely transparent, or see-through.

Squat Lobster
This small lobster is more related to hermit crabs than true lobsters. A new orange species of squat lobster was discovered in 2012 off the coast of Spain.

Alvin
Deep-sea exploration is only possible with machines like this submersible called *Alvin*. Scientists can send out robots from the main ship to get a closer look, too.

24

Deep-sea White Crab

This crab is small, since the weight of the water above it prevents its body from getting too big.

Eelpout

The eelpout is a long fish with a large pouting mouth. It typically feeds on crabs and lobsters.

Hydrothermal Vent

This chimney-like feature of the ocean floor releases harsh, toxic chemicals. Its smoke can be black or white, depending on the chemicals that are coming out.

Brotula

Some species of this fish that live in deep-water caves don't have eyes since it's too dark to use them.

Vent Clams

These clams can tolerate very high temperatures and the chemicals that come out of the vents.

Giant Tube Worm

This red worm lives inside a hard tube and can grow to be 7 feet tall. It doesn't have a mouth or eyes or other organs.

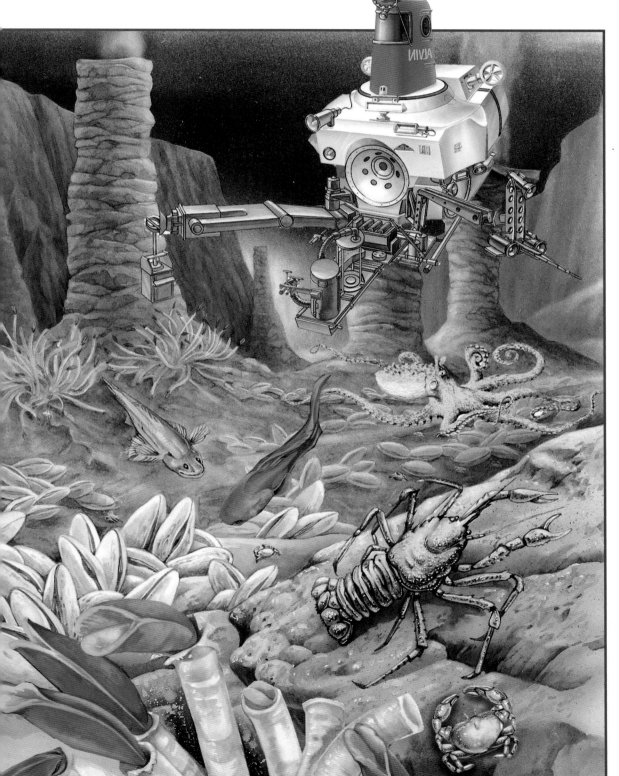

Find Out More
on page 31

Find Out More

Open-Ocean Creatures

After female hawksbill sea turtles hatch from their eggs, they can spend up to thirty years at sea before returning to the same beach to lay their own eggs.

Mahi-mahi are also called dorado or dolphin fish, even though they are not dolphins at all.

Manta rays live deep in the ocean, where they glide through the water and feed on small plants and animals called plankton.

Although they are large and scary-looking, manta rays are gentle creatures that are not harmful to humans.

Squid have soft, squishy bodies without bones.

Squid can move quickly by sucking up water and squirting it out forcefully to propel themselves up to 25 miles per hour!

If squid feel threatened, they can shoot a stream of black ink into the water to confuse predators, then jet away unharmed.

Coral Reef

When corals die, they leave behind skeletons made out of calcium. This hard surface gives other corals a place to live, and the cycle continues, which builds a coral reef.

Lionfish are venomous, which means they have poison in their bodies that they can inject into predators.

Lionfish are naturally found in waters near Australia, but since humans have released them into other parts of the ocean, they are taking over and destroying reefs by eating all of the natural inhabitants.

Did you know that male sea horses carry the babies, not the females? The females give the eggs to the dads to carry until they hatch and swim away.

Sea turtles use coral reefs as a rest area, and also as a cleaning station. There are fish on reefs that actually eat algae from sea turtles' shells, which makes it easier for them to swim through the water.

Deep-Sea Life

Dumbo octopuses are less than 10 inches tall and can live over 1,000 feet below the water surface.

Anglerfish and viperfish have glowing spines on the tops of their heads that wave back and forth to attract prey.

The little that scientists have been able to explore in the deep sea has been done in small submarines like the *Alvin*, pictured in the background.

Even though anglerfish and viperfish can look scary, the anglerfish is only about 5 inches long and the viperfish is only about 11 inches long.

The viperfish has a long body and very sharp, pointy teeth.

The dragonfish has a glowing spine on the bottom of its body instead of on the top, like the anglerfish or viperfish, but uses it in the same way.

Life on the Ocean Bed

Brittle stars are distantly related to sea urchins and sea stars. They are all echinoderms, which means "spiny skin."

Goosefish eggs are held together in a white ribbon that looks like a bride's veil.

Very few animals can eat urchins, since they are protected by hundreds of spines and hard outer shells.

Sharks and More

Sharks lose their teeth often. They have up to twenty rows of them and probably never run out of back-ups.

Great white sharks are highly endangered; experts say that there may be fewer than 3,500 left.

Sawfish use their "saws," called rostrums, to catch prey. They can use them to spear fish or to search for animals on the seafloor.

Hammerhead sharks' eyes are set so far apart that they may be able to see in all directions.

The megalodon shark is an extinct species of shark. Their fossil teeth are 7 inches long, and their bodies were probably over 50 feet long!

Whales

The blue whale is the largest animal on Earth. Baby blue whales are more than three times the size of an average car.

Baleen whales make long song-like sounds that can carry for hundreds of miles.

Toothed whales communicate in a series of clicks and whistles. They use echolocation, like bats, to find food and communicate with one another.

Beluga whales are known as sea canaries since they are often clicking and squealing, sounding much like birds.

Humpback whales give birth in warm tropical waters since their babies are born without their protective layer of fat, called blubber. When the babies have enough blubber, the whole family travels to the cold waters of the North Atlantic to feed.

Seashore

Organisms that live in tide pools have amazing adaptations that allow them to survive both in the air and when they are completely covered with seawater.

Snails have a trapdoor called an operculum that they shut to keep out predators and hold water inside their shells.

Mussels and clams will close their shells when out of the water to keep cool and wet inside.

The shallow water and lack of waves in tide pools allow birds to easily eat some of the trapped animals.

The seashore is home to many organisms. The next time you visit the seashore, be sure to look for animals in the tide pools.

Kelp Forest

Plants in the ocean produce 80 percent of the oxygen on Earth, even more than all the rain forests in the world.

Sheepshead have special teeth that allow them to eat spiny urchins without getting hurt.

Spiny urchins are vegetarians with sharp teeth underneath their bodies that they use to graze on the kelp.

Urchins don't have brains!

Antarctic Waters

Chinstrap penguins prefer to make their nests on rocky areas that do not have any snow.

Baby chinstrap penguins are fed by their parents for about two months before learning to eat by themselves.

Male southern elephant seals can grow to be five times bigger than the females. The males can weigh up to 9,000 pounds, and the females can weigh up to 2,000 pounds.

Weddell seals usually eat fish and squid, but they do also feed on penguins.

Hydrothermal Vents

In 1977, scientists discovered the very first hydrothermal vent (also called a black smoker) in the submersible *Alvin*.

A hydrothermal vent is just like an underwater version of Old Faithful, the hot water geyser in Yellowstone National Park.

Brotulas are some of the few fish in the world that give birth to live young instead of laying eggs.

Many animals that live this deep are small, since being big is almost impossible where the water pressure is so great.

Bacteria live in the skin of giant tube worms and use the chemicals from the vents to make food, which the tube worms can then absorb.

When animals and plants die in the ocean, their cells fall through the water and land in the deep ocean. This "ocean snow" feeds the organisms that live in the deep sea.